From Walker to the World

Charles Mitchell's Low Walker Shipyard

And she stirs!
She starts – she moves – she seems to feel
The thrill of life along the keel,
And spurning with her foot the ground
With one exulting joyous bound,
She leaps into the ocean's arms.

(Longfellow)

Dick Keys and Ken Smith

~Sponsored by A&P Tyne~

Newcastle Libraries & Information Service

Acknowledgements

The authors wish to thank the following: A&P Tyne for providing generous sponsorship; Neil Benson, Executive Editor, Newcastle Chronicle & Journal Ltd., for kindly granting permission to use quotations from old copies of company newspapers; and the staff of Newcastle Libraries & Information Service Local Studies Section for their help and co-operation in research and preparation.

Newcastle Libraries & Information Service gratefully acknowledge A&P Tyne's sponsorship of this book.

Photographic acknowledgements

All photographs are copyright of Newcastle Libraries & Information Service except for the following which are reproduced by kind permission:
Page 6, *Shipping World & Shipbuilder*; page 19, Illustrated London News Picture Library; page 39, Dick Keys; page 44, John Clarkson, Longton.

City of Newcastle upon Tyne
Community & Leisure Services Department
Newcastle Libraries & Information Service

ISBN: 1 85795 038 0

Cataloguing-in-Publication Data: a catalogue record for this book is available from the British Library.

Printed by Bailes the Printer, Houghton-le-Spring.

The front cover illustration shows the launch of the powerful icebreaker *Yermack*, dubbed the 'Walker oyster-opener', at Low Walker in October 1898.

The back cover illustration, from *Le Monde Illustré* 15 April 1899, shows *Yermack* greeted by cheering crowds as she arrives at Kronstadt, near St Petersburg, in 1899 after her maiden voyage from the Tyne.

Cover design by A.V. Flowers.

Also by Dick Keys and Ken Smith:
Down Elswick Slipways: Armstrong's Ships and People 1884-1918, Newcastle City Libraries, 1996.

By Ian Rae and Ken Smith:
Swans of the Tyne, Newcastle City Libraries with North Tyneside Libraries, 1994.
Built with Pride: Tyne Ships 1969-1994, Newcastle City Libraries, 1995.

By Ken Smith:
Turbinia: the Story of Charles Parsons and his Ocean Greyhound, Newcastle Libraries & Information Service with Tyne & Wear Museums, 1996.

Contents

Illustrations

Birth of a Shipyard

*Charles Mitchell, founder of the Low Walker Yard, Newcastle. His first ship was the steam clipper **Havilah**, launched in 1853.*

On March 26 1853 an advertisement appeared in the *Newcastle Daily Journal* stating that the "splendid new clipper ship *Havilah*" would leave Newcastle Quay on 7 April bound for Melbourne, Australia, with a call being made at London on the way.

The advertisement went on: "This vessel has very superior accommodation for a few first class passengers, her fittings being most elegant and complete. All cabin requisites, including beds, bedding etc. will be supplied. Wines, spirits and malt liquors can be had on board at moderate prices."

The *Havilah*, although carrying a spread of sails, also had a steam engine linked to a propeller. This "handsome iron screw steamer", as the newspaper described her, had been launched on 12 February of that year. She was the first ship from a new yard at Low Walker, Newcastle, set up by Charles Mitchell, a hard-working native of Aberdeen who was determined to establish himself as a shipbuilder on the Tyne.

Charles first arrived in Newcastle from Scotland in 1842 and had entered the employment of John Coutts, a pioneer of iron shipbuilding on the river who also owned a yard at Low Walker. Charles, who was a skilled draughtsman, stayed with Coutts for two years, gaining valuable experience, and then moved south to London to work for a firm of marine engineers, Maudslay, Sons and Field, of Lambeth.

In 1852, however, he returned to the Tyne to set up his own yard at Low Walker next to the one which had been operated by Coutts, who had by then moved on. The *Havilah* proved to be the first ship in a long line of vessels launched by Charles Mitchell & Co. and succeeding firms which occupied the yard.

On 19 February 1853 the *Newcastle Journal* gave its readers a detailed description of the *Havilah's* particulars when announcing the launch of the ship, stating that she was of 344 tons, barque rigged and that her hold was 12ft 6ins deep. Readers also learned that she was to be "taken to Messrs. Hawks, Crawshay & Sons for the purpose of receiving her engines which are of the most approved construction, both as regards design and workmanship".

The newspaper indicated that the voyage to Melbourne was partly aimed at those potential passengers seeking to make their fortunes in the gold fields of Australia: "She is built for Messrs. Charles and John F. Bowman, of Leman Street, London, and is shortly to proceed with first class passengers, having been elegantly fitted out for the purpose, to Port Phillip (Melbourne), and the gold regions under the command of Capt. H. McMeckan, who is also part owner."

The *Havilah* went on to become a pioneer steamship in Australian coastal waters and changed ownership several times. She was broken up at Sydney in 1911 after a long and useful life.

In its account of the *Havilah* the *Journal* also told its readers: "Messrs. Mitchell and Co., have on the stocks another screw steamer of larger dimensions than the *Havilah*, and are about laying down a large steamer for the Mediterranean trade." The Mediterranean ship was the *Cagliari*, launched in October 1853 for Sardinian owners to carry salt between the ports of Cagliari and Genoa. Rigged as a three-masted schooner, her engines were supplied by Robert Stephenson & Co., of Newcastle.

Two other ships were also completed at the Low Walker Yard during that first year of business. They were the steam-driven colliers *Vulcan* and *Will o' the Wisp*, which were employed taking North-East coal to Ireland.

Charles Mitchell's new shipyard had clearly got off to a good start and soon it was a flourishing concern. In the early years of its life steam colliers proved to be a mainstay of the order books. Of the first sixteen ships built, eleven were for the

coal trade. It was a time when the old sailing collier brigs were rapidly being replaced by screw steamers which were faster, more reliable and had a greater cargo capacity than the sailing colliers.

In January 1856 one of the Mitchell-built colliers, the *General Codrington*, made the round passage from the Tyne to London and back in four days, seven hours, which at that date was the fastest passage ever made on the route. She had carried 600 tons of coal. It would have taken two sailing colliers about a month to equal this performance.

However, not all of the yard's early ships had successful careers. For example, the collier *Will o' the Wisp*'s life was cut short when in February 1855 she hit a rock off the eastern coast of Ireland during a snowstorm. There were no survivors. She had been bound from Newcastle to Dublin with coals and had been carrying passengers.

On 23 February 1856 Mitchell's yard was the scene of a triple launch witnessed by a large number of spectators. The first vessel to slide down the ways was the 76-ton screw steam yacht *George Robert*, built for a Mr George Bidder, of London. The engine for the vessel was supplied by Messrs. R.

Stephenson and Company of Newcastle.

Next came the *Paris,* a 200ft-long steamer intended for service carrying passengers and cargo between Hamburg and Le Havre. The third ship was the *Eupatoria,* a steam collier whose engines also came from Stephenson and Company's works.

In May 1854 Charles Mitchell had married Anne Swan, of West Farm, Walker, and the couple moved into a house close to the Low Walker Yard. Later, after a spell in the south of

Henry F. Swan, managing partner at the yard and pioneer of oil tanker design.

(**The Shipbuilder**, *Vol. 2, 1907-8*)

England, they settled in Jesmond, Newcastle, where the financially successful Charles bought a mansion which he named Jesmond Towers. The couple had three sons, but only one survived, Charles William, who became an accomplished artist.

By about 1860 Charles Mitchell's brother-in-law, Henry F. Swan, had joined the company as an employee, eventually becoming a partner in the business. The Low Walker Yard went from strength to strength, in particular pioneering the development of oil tankers and producing a wide variety of other vessels.

Although undergoing several changes of ownership and experiencing the effects of the Depression in the early 1930s, the yard did not finally close until 1948, making it one of the longest surviving shipbuilding bases on the Tyne.

Over a period of ninety-five years the Low Walker Yard built 351 screw steamers (mainly cargo ships), 145 oil tankers, seventy-six passenger vessels, six icebreakers, seven train ferries (some with an icebreaking capability), four suction dredgers, six steam yachts, twenty-one gunboats, eleven cruisers, two coast defence battleships, three customs cruisers and five sailing ships. Numerous paddle steamers and barges were also launched.

These ships were produced for many nations. The list includes Britain, Russia, Turkey, Germany, Australia, France, Italy, Egypt, India, Norway, Holland, China, Japan, Brazil, Belgium, Spain, Canada, Romania and Chile.

Ships which went from Walker to the world helped Charles Mitchell make profits which paid for the building of a hospital and a Mechanics' Institute and Hall at Walker and for the building and decoration of St George's Church, Jesmond. The landmark bell-tower of St George's, which can be seen from many parts of Newcastle, is the direct result of the often hard and dangerous work carried out by the men of the Low Walker Yard and of the energy and brilliance of Charles Mitchell.

Disaster on the Slipway

Frequent accidents in the shipyards of the Tyne, including his own, turned Charles' mind to the importance of providing prompt medical attention for injured workmen. Accordingly, he paid for the construction of the Walker Infirmary, a cottage hospital which could treat the casualties. The cost was £2,000. The Infirmary became known as the Walker Accident Hospital and later as the Walker Park Hospital.

This important new medical facility was officially opened in May 1870 by the Mayor of Newcastle, James Morrison, in the presence of members of his council and the local board of health.

In those days the hospital had sixteen beds, which could be increased to twenty in an emergency. Its first surgeon was Dr James R. Lownds who gave his services free of charge. The first matron was a Miss Raynes.

Charles was present at the opening ceremony and he told the gathering that it was proposed that each workman in Walker contribute a penny ha'penny per week towards the maintenance of the hospital.

The first patient was Patrick Butler who had suffered a fractured leg when he fell from staging placed against the side of a ship in one of the yards.

But it was not long before the new hospital had to deal with a major tragedy. In October 1870 six men were killed at the Low Walker Yard as they worked on riveting the keel of the French steamer *Transit*. The ship had moved about three feet down the slipway, crushing the men beneath.

The Newcastle Daily Chronicle told readers: "Yesterday afternoon, about half past three o'clock, a number of men were engaged beneath the keel, which they were riveting, when some of the blocks … slipped from beneath the ship, and the hull being inclined, as all vessels are in the course of construction, towards the river, slid gradually down sternwards for a distance of three feet, settling upon the ground and crushing and mutilating the men beneath her in the most frightful manner.

"There was an entire absence of noise created by the moving of the ship, which sank down quietly to the ground, and in such an easy manner that any casual passer-by would not have observed any movement in the vessel or that she was in any other than her proper position. The groans and agonising cries of the poor fellows beneath the heavy mass of iron were, however, sufficient to alarm and arrest the attentions of the whole of the men on the premises, who hurried at once to the scene of the disaster."

The newspaper added that several persons outside the yard heard the "piteous cries for help" and raised the alarm, a large number of men, women and children then flocking to the gates. Readers learned that "the men were so tightly jammed against the earth and blocks by the weight of the vessel that their extraction would be attended with considerable difficulty … John Crozier, the head foreman of the yard, lost no time in organising a band of willing workers who set about digging the unfortunate sufferers from beneath the keel".

The injured and dying men were then carried to the new hospital where they were received by Dr Lownds and his assistant, a Mr Wilson.

The Walker Accident Hospital, opened in 1870 to treat workers injured in shipyard and factory accidents. Charles Mitchell paid for the hospital to be built.

William Johnson, aged twenty-eight, riveter, single, of Earsdon, but lodging in Victoria Street, Walker. He was dug out from beneath the ship and "so severe were his injuries that he expired while being taken to the Infirmary".

Michael Adams, aged thirty-five, a riveter, married with three children between three and five years old, of Gibson Street, Newcastle. He also died on the way to hospital.

James Kelly, aged twenty-six, a riveter, single, of Byker Street, Walker. He was found crushed to death beneath the vessel.

Joseph Newark, aged twenty-five, riveter, married with one child aged two, of High Friar Street, Newcastle. This unfortunate man was identified by his clothing.

At least one worker in the vicinity lived to tell the tale. A boy employed in carrying the heated rivets escaped unhurt. A tin can from which he had been drinking was completely flattened.

An inquest into the tragedy reached the conclusion that "the ship moved and sank owing to want of sufficient support by bilge blocks and other shores, and, further, that sufficient care had not been exercised by the managers and foreman in charge of the ship".

Clearly, the little hospital at Walker was, as Charles Mitchell had realised, a much needed facility. Also, fatal accidents continued to occur. For example, in June 1890 an inquest was held at the Walker Mechanics' Institute into the death of Thomas Ivory, a plater who was secretary of the local lodge of the Boilermakers' Society. He had died at the hospital on 13

The men who died as a result of the accident were:

Thomas Ferries, aged twenty-eight, a riveter, single, of Walker, who had suffered severe head injuries. He died in the hospital with his mother at his bedside. The newspaper reported that "this unfortunate woman has within the past few weeks lost her husband and son, both of whom met violent deaths at the same yard".

John Yeoman, age variously given as forty-five and fifty-two, a foreman carpenter, married with a grown up family. He received a fracture of the thigh and contusion of the abdomen. He too died in the new Infirmary.

June from injuries received the day before as a result of a fall at the Low Walker Yard. Thomas Ivory left a wife and three children.

Mr J.R.D. Lynn, Coroner for South Northumberland, commented "that many a time he had been struck with the carelessness that existed during the construction of ships, and there seemed to be more carelessness with regard to life and limb in that trade than in any other manufacture he knew of, and he supposed it was chiefly owing to the men's eagerness to get on with their work and make as much money as possible".

After this accident an Ambulance Corps was formed by volunteers at the yard to administer first aid.

Two years later, in August 1892, the newspaper was again reporting on an inquest into a death at the shipyard. The tragic worker was John Potter, aged thirty, of St Peter's, Newcastle. "John Ward, shipwright, stated that he was on the main deck staging (scaffolding) and saw the body come quickly over the top staging, and fall to the ground." His impression was that John Potter had caught his foot against a nut, slipped and had fallen over the ship's side. Catherine Holmes, a nurse at the Walker Hospital, said that the man had died from a fractured skull.

In November 1897 John Rutherford, a plater's helper, was assisting with the fixing of a plate on the side of a vessel when the plate "gave a sudden jerk", knocking the unfortunate man off the staging to the ground about thirty feet below. He was given first aid by the yard Ambulance Corps and taken to the hospital.

A particularly sad and heart-rending accident occurred in May 1902 when a fourteen-year-old boy was killed. He also fell to his death from staging. The inquest was held at the Stack Hotel, Walker. John Dodds, of Church Street, Walker, identified the body as that of his son, Matthew.

The boy was working as a rivet heater and fell from the main deck of a vessel on to some staging five feet below.

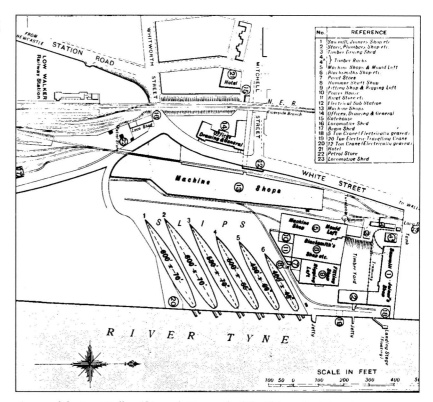

A map of the Low Walker Shipyard, Newcastle. (The Shipyards of Armstrong Whitworth)

Tragically, he bounced off this structure and fell again, this time plummeting twenty feet to the bottom of the ship. Matthew died before the men could carry him from the vessel. Returning a verdict of accidental death, the inquest jury "were of the opinion that the employment of three young boys was too hazardous and that the age should be increased from the present age of 14". Once again, shipbuilding had proved to be a highly dangerous occupation.

Trouble and Strife

Like the other shipyards on the Tyne, Mitchell's at Low Walker had its fair share of strikes and industrial disputes. One of the most unusual of these occurred in July 1869 when two Irish labourers refused to work overtime. The reaction of their foreman or "gaffer" to this decision sparked a strike.

A large number of Irishmen were employed to carry iron plates for the ships to the platers. The trouble began after several of the platers were requested to work overtime. One of them, a man named Sheely, spoke to two of the labourers and asked them if they would put in the extra hours. The labourers refused, saying they lived at South Shields and if they worked overtime it would cause them great inconvenience and expense since they would miss the ferry down river.

Mr Sheely, no doubt finding himself in a difficult position, did the only thing he could and told the foreman of the yard, Mr Coulson, about the situation and asked for two other assistants. Coulson, an Englishman, then inquired why the men would not work overtime and Sheely replied that they lived a considerable distance away from the works and would miss their passage on the boat home.

Mr Coulson then asked the plater for the names of the two labourers but Mr Sheely said he was unable to give the information. The foreman inquired if they were Irishmen and was told they were. Coulson was said to have replied: "If they are two Irishmen and will not oblige me by going on tonight, they need not come in tomorrow."

Mr Sheely reported these remarks to the two labourers who considered that their gaffer had used the term "Irishmen" in an offensive way. News of the remarks spread to the other Irish workers, sparking anger and discontent. Within a few days 160 of them were on strike, calling for the dismissal of the foreman.

The company accused the men of breaking the rules under which they were engaged. These rules had been read to them before they were taken on and included the requirement to give a fortnight's notice if they wished to leave. The men did not dispute this, but replied that three days before the strike the foreman had dismissed two Irishmen without giving them notice and if the masters could break the rules with impunity why should the rules be binding upon the men?

The Irishmen said they were satisfied with their wages and hours. Their only complaint was the insult from the gaffer and the fact that two of them had been dismissed without proper notice.

Summonses were then served on thirteen of the men for leaving their employer without giving the required notice. The strikers then sent a deputation to Charles Mitchell, in the hope of reaching a peaceful solution to the dispute. Charles was told of the foreman's words and he said that if the men would return to work and pay the costs incurred up to that time, the summonses would be withdrawn. But the men refused to accept this offer and remained on strike.

The unlucky thirteen labourers therefore duly appeared before Newcastle magistrates at the Moot Hall Police Court. By this time they had told a solicitor they would return to work if the prosecution was withdrawn. The solicitor, a Mr Joel, told the Bench that the men wished to go back.

The Newcastle Daily Chronicle reported: "He had to promise, on behalf of the men, that if they wished to leave after this misunderstanding they would give the required 14 days' notice. Whether they had or had not any ground for complaint he would not take it upon himself to say; but it appeared to him that the proper course to take, as he had advised his clients, was to lay their grievances before their employers and not all leave in a body without having given notice."

The newspaper's readers learned that Mr W.S. Daglish, prosecuting, told the court he had no wish to press the case with severity against any of the men. His remarks were at variance with the men's earlier account of matters. Mr Daglish contended that Charles Mitchell and Co. had always strictly observed the rules on their side and "though it might often be to their advantage to be able to dismiss some of their workmen without notice, they had never yet done so".

The attractive paddle ferry **Audrey** *passes the North Pier lighthouse at the entrance to the Tyne on her return from a pleasure trip. The* **Audrey,** *and her sister, the* **Aileen,** *were both built at Low Walker for the Tyne General Ferry Company. They were launched in 1897.*

Both sides had rattled their sabres at one another but the heat was rapidly disappearing from the argument. With the promise of the men to return to work the dispute was over and the magistrates took no action against them.

Many other disputes, of course, concerned pay and hours of work. In early 1904, for example, a scarcity of orders resulted in three-quarter-time working for the men at Low Walker. This enabled the company to employ a greater number of workers, but the short-time arrangement was unpopular, since it naturally led to loss of wages. The men claimed the firm had more work in hand than any other yard on the North-East Coast on short-time.

The men had understood that full-time working would be resumed on 1 February 1904 but when they reached the yard that morning they were told they were still on three-quarter-time. The workers then held a meeting outside the gates and decided they would not return to their employment unless the management agreed to reinstate full-time hours. Mitchell's refused to see a deputation to discuss the situation "owing to the irregularity of the proceedings".

Punitive action was not slow in coming. The masters imposed a week's lock-out on the men who had attended the meeting. At the same time, however, Mitchell's told them that after the lock-out had ended they could go back to full-time. It was a mixture of retaliation and concession. No doubt the lock-out reduced the wages bill for a week. But the craftsmen and labourers were warned that full-time working would mean the employment of less men. This appears to have been accepted without major protest.

If a man's job on a ship came to an end and there was no other work, he and his fellow workmen would be laid off until their services were needed again. In such circumstances they would go in search of employment at another yard and, if they were lucky, find it. Men were helped in their search for jobs by the existence, from 1862 to 1908, of a ferry boat service up and down the river between Newcastle and North Shields. Owned by the Tyne General Ferry Company, the paddle steamers which ran on this route connected the various shipyards both north and south of the river.

Steamers left Newcastle Quayside at regular intervals throughout the day, calling at the mouth of the Ouseburn, St Peter's, High Felling, Bill Quay, High Walker, Low Walker, Hebburn, Carville (Wallsend), Hebburn Colliery, Howdon, Jarrow, Howdon Dock, Tyne Dock, Mill Dam, North Shields Landing and North Shields Fish Quay. In the summer, the service was extended to the North and South Piers at the mouth of the Tyne for those enjoying their leisure. There were also pleasure excursions to the coastal waters off Northumberland.

By the time the Tyne General Ferry Company's services ended in 1908 it owned a fleet of sixteen boats and in its final year carried five million passengers. About half this figure represented workmen travelling to and from the shipyards each day.

The ferry company provided the Low Walker Yard with orders. The yard built three of its paddle steamers, the *Phoebe*, launched in 1895, and the *Audrey* and *Aileen*, both dating from 1897.

The steel-hulled *Phoebe* slid down the ways into the Tyne on 14 March 1895. Her paddle engines were fitted by the Wallsend Slipway & Engineering Company. *The Newcastle Daily Journal* reported: "On leaving the ways the vessel was gracefully named *Phoebe* by Miss Rea, daughter of Mr Jas. Rea, secretary of the owners."

The 126ft-long *Audrey* was launched at Low Walker on 2 May 1897. "The comfort of the passengers has been carefully provided for in all the arrangements of the vessel," the newspaper declared. The boat was "designed for the purpose of sea excursions as well as river service; and a refreshment bar, a tea buffet, and good lavatory accommodation has been provided. Passengers to the number of 600 can be carried on the river service and about 250 at sea, so that summer excursions to the Farne Islands and other places of interest along our coast will no doubt become extremely popular". At the launch the steamer was named *Audrey* by Mrs J.E. Rogerson, the wife of Mr J.E. Rogerson, a director of the Tyne General Ferry Company.

The last of the trio from Low Walker, the *Aileen*, entered the Tyne on 17 June 1897. A sister vessel to the *Audrey*, she was also to be used as a passenger excursion steamer as well as a day-to-day ferry. The christening ceremony was performed by Kitty Swan, daughter of Henry F. Swan.

It is intriguing to think that some of the Low Walker workers who built these boats would have gone on to regularly use them for travelling up and down river and even, perhaps, for summer excursions to the North Sea.

Steam Yachts and Millionaires

Steam yachts were elegant and often luxurious examples of the shipbuilder's art. Constructed for the private use of wealthy customers, they were essentially the pleasure boats of millionaires, aristocrats and princes. Charles Mitchell's Low Walker Yard built several of these vessels during its early years, the first, as we have seen, being the *George Robert* of 1856.

Ten years later, in 1866, another steam yacht was completed at Low Walker, the *Northumbria,* built for George Robert Stephenson, head of the firm of Robert Stephenson & Co, of Forth Banks, Newcastle. In fact, Stephenson's provided the reciprocating engines for the vessel and these drove a four-bladed propeller. In addition, the *Northumbria* carried sails on three masts.

The Newcastle Daily Chronicle described her as "rakish looking, moulded on the finest lines" and she featured a figurehead, described as a beautiful female figure holding a miner's pick in one hand and a lump of coal in the other. Her crew of thirteen seamen were "picked men from Cowes" dressed in blue uniforms with white facings and gilt buttons adorned with an anchor. The front of their caps carried the word *Northumbria* in gilt letters.

"The motive which Mr Stephenson had in ordering this beautiful yacht had its origins quite apart from its employment as a means of healthy recreation," the *Chronicle* told its readers. "His principal object is, we understand, to show the southern yacht owners that the Tyne can produce specimens of naval architecture in this highly ornamental class of vessel equal to those constructed in any port of the kingdom."

The vessel was launched into the Tyne by Miss Isabella Stephenson, the eldest daughter of the owner, who broke a bottle of champagne over the yacht's bows in traditional fashion, christening her the *Northumbria*. Evidently, the owner's daughters wore dresses which echoed those of the seamen: "The Misses Stephenson were dressed in singularly beautiful yachting attire – a French white trimmed with blue and gilt buttons".

The weather was cool owing to an easterly wind but it seemed to have no effect on the enjoyment of the event by spectators. Not surprisingly, those present included the wealthy Mr Stephenson, nephew of railway locomotive pioneer George Stephenson. Keeping a close eye on the proceedings to see that all went smoothly was Henry F. Swan, by then a managing partner at the yard.

The Stephenson works band played the *Keel Row* as the yacht began to move down the ways, followed by *Rule Britannia* after she was afloat. Once the ceremony was over the official guests were treated to lunch in the draughting loft. This meal was "an elegant lunch supplied by Mr Jeffries of the Central Station Hotel".

The *Northumbria* had been designed by a Mr Dobson, Mitchell's foreman shipwright, who was presented with a gold watch by Stephenson. A silver watch was presented to a Mr McLauchlan for the "excellent manner in which he had executed the joinery work".

Stephenson was clearly delighted with his new steam yacht for he provided £150 to pay for dinner for the workmen employed at the yard, with the proviso that the meal take place

The barque-rigged steam yacht **Cumbria**, *built at Low Walker in 1881 for the Earl of Lonsdale, of Lowther Castle, Westmorland. Here, the* **Cumbria** *is lying in the Tyne.*

large company went to the river side to watch the vessel slide into the water, which she did in splendid style. She was named the *General Kotzebue*.

"After the launch was disposed of and when the men had time to get themselves cleaned up, they assembled at the gates of the yard where a procession was formed headed by the band of the 8th Northumberland Volunteers of Walker … The banners belonging to the boilermakers also gave a picturesque appearance to the procession which paraded through the principal parts of the town before they went to dinner."

About 800 men were given the meal, including senior staff members of Mitchell's and Stephenson's along with officials of the Russian Steam Navigation Co. These senior figures "sat down to a sumptuous repast at the house of Mr Carr, Woolsington Arms, near the railway station". The large number of diners, as well as perhaps the social distinctions of the era, meant that the men had to be divided into groups, with each group being given their meal at different public houses, inns and hotels.

during Newcastle's Race Week.

On 26 June 1866 the *Chronicle* reported that "in order that the men might thoroughly enjoy themselves" they were "paid off for the week yesterday dinner time, thus giving them the rest of the week for a holiday. To add to the festivities, the Messrs. Mitchell had fixed the launching of a powerful and beautiful paddle steamer intended for the Black Sea service and built for the Russian Steam Navigation Company. A very

The 130 men of the joinery department went to "Mr Reay, Scrogg House"; sixty chippers and caulkers ate at the "house of Mr Crawford, Colliery Inn"; 200 boilermakers, platers and shipwrights sat down to their dinner at the "house of John Tweddle, New Stack Hotel"; the 100 smiths, riggers, sail makers, saw mill men and yacht crew dined at "Mrs Curry's Victoria Hotel"; and forty-three plumbers and painters enjoyed their meal at the house of "Mr Cooley, Ship Inn". The *Chronicle* added that "a number of songs were sung, and the proceedings were of a most hilarious and pleasant character". Clearly, it seems that a good time was had by all. The event also illustrates the high value of the pound in 1866 – a meal for 800 people had been provided at a cost of £150!

The *Northumbria* was by no means the last steam yacht to be launched at the Low Walker Yard. Two examples of this type of vessel named the *Nora* came from its slipways. The first *Nora*, like the second, was built for Mons. Jean Baptiste Perret, a wealthy French Senator of Lyons, but she was wrecked off St Mary's Island, Whitley Bay, on 24 April 1879 while undergoing trials.

On board for this trial trip were representatives of the shipbuilders, engine builders and owner. They included Henry F. Swan and Dobson, who had risen to become yard manager. The steam yacht had just completed a satisfactory run on the measured mile and was being turned around to steam back to the Tyne when she hit the wreck of the steamer *Longhirst*, a short distance to the north of St Mary's Island. There was no buoy marking the wreck. The bottom of the yacht's hull was torn open and she began sinking fast. The *Nora* went down by the head, her propeller being lifted out of the water as she did so.

The forty-four crew and passengers on board had only a short time to get into the boats but fortunately these were ready for launching. A young man was in the propeller tunnel oiling the machinery when the accident happened and he had great difficulty escaping as the engine room began filling with water. Luckily, however, he managed to reach the open deck and survived along with everyone else.

One of the survivors had to keep his thumb in the plug hole of a lifeboat to prevent it sinking until a plug could be found. There was a heavy swell hitting the shore of the island but the boats managed to find a safe place to land. It had been a narrow escape for all concerned.

In December 1879 a second *Nora* was launched at Low Walker to replace her wrecked predecessor. Both vessels had been named after Mons. Perret's Irish wife. The second yacht was larger than the first. She was 170ft long and featured a clipper bow with a female figurehead and, as was usually the case, an elaborately carved stern. Her engines were supplied by R. & W. Hawthorn, of Newcastle. Her cabin accommodation was described as "sumptuous" with room for eight guests. There was an owner's suite, lounge, music room, and dining room. Upholstery and decorations were French in style.

Among other steam yachts from Low Walker was the *Cumbria*, built in 1881 for the Earl of Lonsdale, of Lowther Castle, Westmorland. The *Cumbria* was certainly a most remarkable yacht, constructed and fitted out regardless of expense. A shapely clipper bow was crowned by a figurehead of a dragon rampant and the stern was decorated with carved woodwork. Accommodation for the owner and his guests was described as "beautiful" and there was even a doctor's room on board.

The vessel carried four two-and-a-quarter-inch guns, although it is not recorded why such warlike fittings were considered necessary. Her steam compound surface condensing engines were supplied by the Wallsend Slipway and Engineering Co. Ltd., giving her a speed of 11 knots. The vessel also carried a fine array of square sails.

She was indeed impressive, but Lord Lonsdale did not live long to enjoy his wonderful steam yacht. He died suddenly in 1882 only a year after the *Cumbria* was delivered.

*Elegant princess. The Low Walker steam yacht **Nora** passes down the Tyne. This vessel, launched in December 1879, was the second **Nora**, being a replacement for a steam yacht of the same name wrecked off St Mary's Island, Whitley Bay, in April 1879.*

Tugs for Siberia

In the summer of 1894 two powerful paddle tugs, the *Pervoi* and *Vtori,* were completed at the Low Walker Yard. They were designed for towing service on the River Yenisei and its tributaries in the middle of Siberia with the object of delivering materials for the Trans-Siberian Railway.

The currents of some of these rivers are extremely rapid and in addition to paddle machinery the tugs were also fitted with large hauling engines which were designed so that each tug could haul herself and barges up the rapids by means of a chain which was laid into the river bed. The vessels were also equipped with powerful gearing on deck and separate engines to work the gearing. Before being delivered to Russia, chains were laid in the Tyne to test this ingenious equipment.

The main engines were in duplicate and arranged so that the two paddle wheels on each vessel could be worked independently of each other, and even in opposite directions for greater convenience in handling. These engines were of 600 horsepower and the boilers were constructed for burning wood as fuel.

Novel and powerful these steamers certainly were, but the task of delivering them from the Tyne to Siberia was a tricky one. The River Yenisei flows northwards across Siberia into the Arctic waters of the Kara Sea, which are icebound for much of the year. The delivery voyage thus required a captain who knew the route around the North Cape of Norway and through the seas of the Russian Arctic.

Such a seaman was Captain Joseph Wiggins, the former Board of Trade examiner in seamanship for the Sunderland and South Shields areas. Born in Norfolk, he had served in sailing ships of the North-East Coast and had married a Sunderland girl. Wiggins had helped to open up a trading route into the Kara Sea, giving access to the mouths of the Ob and Yenisei rivers and enabling ships to bring back timber, furs and other cargoes from Siberia.

Accordingly, on 8 August 1894 a small flotilla of ships left the Tyne bound for the Russian Arctic and under the overall command of Captain Wiggins. It consisted of the Low Walker tugs *Pervoi* and *Vtori* and the Arctic yacht *Blencathra*, owned by Hugh Popham, a well-known yachtsman. At a port on the Norwegian coast they were met by the wooden steamer *Stjernen*, which it was planned would return the crews of the vessels to Britain.

All went well with the outward voyage and Wiggins successfully delivered the Tyne-built tugs to the Russian authorities at a place called Lokovoi Protok some 500 miles up the Yenisei. He and the delivery crews left there on 15 September of that year for the voyage home in the *Stjernen*. Then they disappeared for nearly four months before details of their escape from shipwreck became known to the outside world.

They had reached the Kara Sea safely but later the *Stjernen* had hit a reef off the coast of the Yamal Peninsula during dense fog. This fog persisted and the wind became stronger. The damaged ship settled broadside onto the rocks in a heavy swell. The situation was now so serious that Wiggins gave the order to abandon ship and with difficulty the crews were safely landed on the barren shores of the Yamal Peninsula, home to the Samoyed people of northern Siberia. Hugh Popham and three other men volunteered to walk to the settlement of

*The Russian paddle tugs **Pervoi** and **Vtori** lying in the Tyne before their departure for the River Yenisei, Siberia.*

and the Samoyeds also gave them their spare tents for shelter at night.

Wiggins and his men travelled for thirty-two days for between 500 and 600 miles across the frozen tundra accompanied and guided by the Samoyeds and 2,000 head of reindeer. By 17 November all the party of forty-nine men had reached Pustozersk on the Petchora River. Two men were suffering badly from frostbite and one had to have two or three of his toes amputated.

On 15 December 1894 the crews reached the port of Archangel without mishap, although five men who had been taken ill were admitted to hospital upon arrival. The party learned that two vessels had been sent out, one from Norway and one from the Yenisei, in search of them. Their fate had naturally been the subject of much speculation.

Captain Wiggins later said that the loss of the *Stjernen* was a sea accident which might have happened anywhere in the world and did not in any way discredit the navigability of the sea route to Siberia.

The tugs *Pervoi* and *Vtori* were not the only connections between the Low Walker Yard and the Kara Sea route. Between the First and Second World Wars the Russian icebreaker *Lenin* was often on duty in the Yugorski Strait leading into the southern part of the sea to clear or guide the way for ships heading for the mouths of the Yenisei and the Ob. The *Lenin* had been completed at Low Walker as the *Alexander Nevski* in 1917.

Chabrova to enlist the help of the Samoyeds.

Eventually they reached the tent of a Russian trader named Ivan Koshevin and he set out for the place where the survivors were encamped accompanied by a group of Samoyeds on sledges. Eventually more sledges, pulled by reindeer, arrived to help the seamen as news of their landing spread and most of the provisions aboard the wreck were recovered. It was necessary to take food and other stores from the ship because food was in short supply in Chabrova.

Ivan Koshevin and the Samoyeds showed great kindness to the seamen and it was due to their help that they survived the immense journey that lay ahead of them. Fur suits and other outfits made from reindeer skins were provided for the men

Icebreakers and Train Ferries

In 1882 Charles Mitchell and Co. of the Low Walker Yard merged with the firm of Sir W.G. Armstrong of Elswick in the West End of Newcastle to become Sir W.G. Armstrong, Mitchell and Co. Ltd. A shipyard was opened at Elswick in 1884 which concentrated on the building of warships, while Low Walker specialised mainly in merchant vessels. The hard-working Charles died in 1895 at the age of seventy-five.

Two years later the company underwent a further amalgamation, this time with the firm of Joseph Whitworth of Manchester, thus forming Sir W.G. Armstrong, Whitworth and Co. Ltd. However, throughout all these business transformations the Low Walker Yard continued to build a great many ships, including a series of icebreakers and train ferries. Russia was to prove one of the main customers for these specialised vessels. By the early 1900s the yard had gained a fine reputation for the building of icebreakers and was at the forefront of their design.

As early as 1856 a Mitchell-built ship had made the news when it tackled ice on a river. The vessel was the *Pollux* which went through ice up to five feet thick on an experimental passage up the Elbe in Germany. Built for a Hamburg firm, the *Pollux*, a screw steamer, had been launched at Low Walker the previous year. However, she was not specifically built as an icebreaker. Her voyage up river was a test to see the extent to which it was possible to keep navigation open during the win-

*The steamer **Pollux** tackles the ice on the River Elbe in 1856. (**Illustrated London News**, 2 February 1856)*

*The **Saratovski Ledokol** tackles the ice on the River Volga. She had been launched at the yard in 1895.*

used to keep a canal open between Kronstadt and Oranienbaum, then a railway terminus on the coast.

Mitchell's took an important step forward in 1895 when the Low Walker Yard launched its first purpose-built icebreaker, the *Saratovski Ledokol*, for service on the River Volga. Her job was to keep a passage open through the ice for a train ferry, the *Saratovskaia Pereprava*, which was also built at the yard.

The icebreaker was transported on barges in two longitudinal sections through the Marinski Canal system to the Volga crossing point of the Riazan-Ouralsk Railway. The ship had to be divided in this way since it was too wide to pass through the canal locks. Similarly, the train ferry was divided, this time into four sections, both longitudinally and transversely, for the passage

ter months. The vessel was trimmed by the stern so that her bow would rise up to crush the ice.

Eight years later, in 1862, Mitchell's completed the *Pilot*, a tug which was to become one of the first true icebreakers. Again, she was not specifically built as such. Constructed for a Russian owner named Britnev, the *Pilot* was used in the waters of the Kronstadt and St Petersburg areas. Around 1870 Britnev had a new, stronger bow built on the vessel so that she could keep a passage open through the ice longer than was usually possible between Kronstadt and St Petersburg. She was also

through the canals. It was an ingenious feat of design and technology.

Reporting on the launch of the *Saratovski Ledokol* in May 1895, the *Newcastle Daily Journal* said that she was "probably the most powerful icebreaker in the world which is intended to be employed in conjunction with a large railway ferry steamer, also building at the same yard, in carrying railway trucks across the River Volga. As it is desired to carry the service throughout the winter, when the ice of the river is of great thickness, it became necessary to provide a very powerful icebreaker. The vessel is 150ft long and 26ft in beam and will be fitted with twin screw engines of 1,400 h.p.". The paper added that "a great deal of the shell plating is as much as an inch thick".

The train ferry *Saratovskaia Pereprava* was launched a month after the icebreaker. *The Newcastle Daily Journal* informed readers that "for loading and discharging the railway trucks a special hydraulic hoist constructed at the Elswick works is to be fitted in the bow of the vessel, arranged in such a way that the trucks may be run on or off the vessel whatever the level of the river". Her structure was also strengthened to enable her to resist the ice.

By early August the train ferry was undergoing trials up and down the Tyne and was evidently the object of attention for many Geordies. The newspaper reported that "during the passage up and down the river she created a good deal of interest, many of the uninitiated wondering what such a vessel could be intended for". Any readers who might still be wondering were informed that she was "intended to carry railway trains across a swift flowing river, the level of which varies to the extent of 40ft between highest and lowest points".

The delivery of these two cleverly constructed vessels was an achievement of great magnitude for the company, but in 1895-98 Mitchell's carried out an even more ambitious project – the delivery of an icebreaking train ferry to the shores of Lake Baikal in the middle of Siberia. The ship, appropriately named the *Baikal*, was designed to carry passengers, carriages and trucks across the lake between two sections of the Trans-Siberian Railway. At that date a line around the southern shores of this huge body of water was still in the planning stage and was not constructed until 1900-1904. Those building this track were faced with rocky and mountainous terrain and this necessitated tunnelling and the building of bridges in sometimes harsh weather conditions.

*The icebreaking train ferry **Baikal** under construction on the shores of Lake Baikal, Siberia. The vessel had been shipped to Russia from Low Walker in thousands of parts.*

*The impressive-looking icebreaking train ferry **Baikal.** Her facilities included a chapel, which became a favourite wedding venue.*

Before the line came into service passengers and freight had therefore to travel across the deep waters of Lake Baikal between Baranchuk on the northern shore to Mysovaya on the southern.

The train ferry *Baikal* was constructed on a slipway at Low Walker, taking under a year to complete. She was then dismantled and the different sections and pieces were marked and shipped from the Tyne to St Petersburg. From there, the parts, which weighed almost 3,000 tons in total, were transported in about 6,900 packages by rail and river to Irkutsk, the largest town near the western side of the lake. It was reported that the items were then carried by pony-drawn sledges to the lake.

The first consignment of sections had left Low Walker in 1896 and only in late 1898 did the last consignment reach its destination, the village of Listvennitchnaya on the lake shore.

The ship was then put together again and launched.

The task of reconstructing the *Baikal* was led by a team of engineers from Tyneside whose journey to Siberia must have been something of an adventure. In charge of the team was Andrew Douie. His assistants were a Mr Renton, an aptly-named Mr Handy and a fourth man.

They lived in the small village of Listvennitchnaya, where robbery and other crimes were said to be commonplace. Few went out after dark and many people carried revolvers for protection.

It was reported that a considerable number of the men working on the rebuilding of the *Baikal* had been transported to Siberia for alleged crimes, including the foreman of the labourers. One man working on the ship was wanted for allegedly killing eight people.

The *Baikal* was launched into the lake in June 1899 and was then towed to Baranchuk for fitting out. By January 1900 she was undergoing trials, successfully tackling ice between eighteen inches and four feet thick. In the summer of that year she at last entered service on her intended route. The project had taken over four years to complete.

The 290ft-long *Baikal* was of 5,280 gross tons and had cabins for 150 passengers. The ship even had her own restaurant. She also featured a chapel, which became a popular place for Siberian couples to hold their weddings.

Her two propulsion engines were of 3,750 horsepower, driving twin propellers. A third engine drove another propeller positioned under the vessel's bow which was designed to cause the ice above to lose much of its natural support so that it would crack more easily as it was crushed by the ship's advancing bows. The four-funnel vessel was adapted to burn wood as fuel. Her steel hull was one-inch thick and backed by nearly two feet of timber.

She carried three lines on her rail deck which were capable of accommodating goods trucks or passenger carriages. The centre track could be used by the large sleeping cars of the Trans-Siberian Express.

Meanwhile, parts for a passenger-carrying icebreaker, to be named the *Angara*, had also been arriving at the lake. This ship too was constructed at the Low Walker Yard, dismantled and shipped out to St Petersburg, thence travelling by rail to the lake shore. By this time the Trans-Siberian Railway had been extended up to the shoreline.

The two-funnel *Angara* was then reassembled, launched and began service in late 1900. However, the train ferry was the more powerful vessel and often helped to clear the way through the ice for the *Angara* when conditions were particularly severe. The two ships carried thousands of the Tsar's troops to the Russo-Japanese War in 1904-05.

The *Baikal* is believed to have been destroyed around 1920 during the Russian Civil War which followed the Revolution of 1917. The *Angara* gained notoriety by becoming the scene of a brutal massacre in the same conflict. In early 1920 forces allied to the White Russian armies seized thirty-one Menshevik socialists and Social Revolutionaries. They were taken aboard the ship and clubbed to death with a mallet as the vessel steamed over the lake. Their bodies were then tossed into the frozen waters.

The *Angara* atrocity angered the people of the Irkutsk area and the unsavoury episode was instrumental in the downfall of Admiral Kolchak, leader of the Whites in Siberia. Even though the forces which carried out the killings were not directly under his control, Kolchak's reputation was tainted by his association with them.

The passenger icebreaker *Angara* is believed to still survive today. She was last reported as laid up on the River Angara near Irkutsk and in the 1980s there were plans to turn her into a floating museum.

In 1899 another icebreaker had been launched at Low Walker. She was the *Ledokol III*, which had been ordered by the port authorities of Odessa on the Black Sea. The 158ft-long vessel was adequate for work in ice of about three feet thick.

The Russian icebreaker **Angara** *cuts through the frozen waters of Lake Baikal, Siberia. She became the scene of a notorious massacre during the Russian Civil War.*

bridge is carried on a series of braced gantries and combined with the funnels to produce a very un-nautical effect." A story was told that when the *Scotia* was running her trials off the North-East coast an onlooker at Hartley, near Blyth, said to a friend: "Whey, Geordie, there's Bedlington Colliery gannin awa' to sea." (See page 29).

The two other train ferries for Canada were the 300ft-long *Prince Edward Island*, of 2,795 gross tons, which was launched in 1914, and the *Scotia II*, of 1,859 gross tons, which entered the Tyne the following year. The appropriately-named *Prince Edward Island* was constructed for service between Prince Edward Island near the Gulf of St Lawrence and the Canadian mainland. The *Scotia II* succeeded the earlier vessel on the Strait of Canso route.

The need for ships to move through ice-bound seas had kept many men in work on the banks of the Tyne.

However, Russia was not the only country which placed orders for icebreakers with the yard. In April 1898 the *Sampo* was launched for Finland. Her main task was to keep the port of Hango open during the winter and also to carry out similar work at Helsinki. Another Finnish icebreaker, the *Tarmo*, was launched by the company in 1907.

In addition, Low Walker built three icebreaking train ferries for service in Canada. The first, the *Scotia*, was constructed for service across the Strait of Canso separating Cape Breton Island from the mainland of Nova Scotia. Completed in 1901, she was an odd looking vessel. Her four funnels were situated on the extreme sides of the ship. Many years later the *Armstrong Whitworth Record* commented: "The navigation

The Walker Oyster-Opener

Perhaps the most impressive of the Low Walker icebreakers was the *Yermack*, built for the Russian government for service in the Baltic, Gulf of Finland and Arctic seas. She is generally regarded as the first icebreaker designed for polar use.

With a displacement of nearly 8,000 tons, the *Yermack* (often referred to as the *Ermack*) was one of the larger ships of her type to be constructed at the yard. The 305ft-long vessel was launched in October 1898. The idea of building the ship was conceived by Vice Admiral Stepan Makarov who believed that a powerful icebreaker should keep the Baltic open for Russian ships during the winter and then steam to the Russian Arctic in the spring where she could force open an early trading passage to the Kara Sea and Siberian rivers while ice still gripped that area.

At the *Yermack*'s launch, Henry F. Swan told guests that Admiral Makarov, besides sketching out the broad principles of the ship, had been of the greatest help to Armstrong Whitworth in working out the technical details. Among those present was Captain Vasiliev, the man who was to take the ship through the Baltic on her delivery voyage to Kronstadt. Madame Vasiliev, the captain's wife, performed the launching ceremony.

The captain was applauded as he told the crowd that the intellect and scientific skill of man would overcome nature and overwhelm the elements. He was convinced that ice in the future would be no more a hindrance to navigation than fogs were at present.

The *Newcastle Daily Chronicle* reported: "The building of this vessel has presented many difficult problems. The hull is divided into no less than 48 compartments, each of which is absolutely watertight." It added: "The launching ceremony was witnessed by an immense crowd of spectators … the vessel glided down the ways without the slightest mishap."

By early March 1899 the *Yermack* was undergoing her first trials off the Tyne. The *Chronicle*, under the heading "The Walker Wonder", stated enthusiastically: "The *Yermack* can only be described as the oyster-opener of the world's marine". She was "massively framed of steel, and so built that instead of smashing against the edge of the ice she will rise with its pressure like Nansen's *Fram* and break it down by weight".

The paper's optimistic tone continued: "In keeping the Baltic open all the year round, the icebreaker will discharge a function remarkable enough. But Admiral Makarov hopes also that the *Yermack* will make a more regular path through the Siberian seas in the track of Capt Wiggins' pioneering voyages; and he is not alone in the idea that the Walker oyster-opener may penetrate even to the North Pole."

The ship left the Tyne on her maiden voyage to Kronstadt on 2 April 1899.

Engineering reported: "Her arrival at Kronstadt was evidently an extraordinary sight. The ice was about 18 inches thick with a good deal of snow on top, and the ship steamed through this at six and a half knots up to the sea wall and past the battleships. She swung round on the port hand and entered the harbour through an entrance only 95 feet wide; the ship, it will be remembered is of 71 feet beam … The outer skin is polished bright where the vessel has been running through the

*The launch of the Russian icebreaker **Yermak** at Low Walker in 1898. Note the distinctive hull shape. On her delivery voyage the following year the ship cut her way through the ice of the Baltic to reach the port of Kronstadt, near St Petersburg, where she was greeted by enthusiastic Russians.*

ice, but there are no signs of leakage anywhere."

Engineering added: "During the progress from Tolbeacon (Tokouchin) Light into the harbour the ship was accompanied by thousands of people on sledges, and the colonel of a regiment, who is a friend of Admiral Makarov, marched out with 60 men on 'ski' to meet the vessel".

Others who made the six-mile journey across the frozen sea to meet the icebreaker included a party of Russian naval officers. The *Yermack* left behind her a wide channel in what was described as a "desert" of ice. Some of the visitors were taken aboard and others rode alongside in sledges, but the small Finland horses had a job keeping up with the vessel. At two o'clock the *Yermack* entered the port of Kronstadt where crowds of enthusiastic people cheered her as she ploughed her way through the ice to the pier.

The *Chronicle* described the *Yermack*'s arrival as "a kind of national event with Admiral Makarov the hero of the day". It said the ship had been "cutting through the thick ice of the Finnish Gulf as easy as a knife goes through butter".

Russia's new icebreaker was

*A bow view of the **Yermack** in the ice. In 1899 she freed many ships trapped in the frozen waters of the Baltic. This impressive icebreaker is believed to have survived until the mid-1960s.*

*A stern view of the Finnish icebreaker **Tarmo** on the stocks at Low Walker before her launch in 1907. With her sister, the **Sampo**, also built at Low Walker, the **Tarmo** proved very successful in keeping the narrow seas off Finland open during the winter months.*

specially formed to resist crushing and a steel belt of twenty-five feet in height on either side of the vessel was fitted with heavy frames spaced a foot apart, supporting flush plating more than an inch thick.

Several months after her delivery the *Yermack* made an experimental voyage to Arctic waters to test her icebreaking capabilities in polar conditions. She proved herself able to break ice up to 20ft thick, but when she came up against ice of 80ft thickness her bows were severely damaged. The ship was forced to return to the Tyne to have a new bow fitted.

By late 1901 she was again back in service and Captain Vasiliev was reporting a successful Arctic voyage to Novaya Zemla and Franz Joseph Land.

In 1904 the Russian Baltic Fleet left Kronstadt for its disastrous encounter with the Japanese at the Battle of Tsushima the following year. The *Yermack* helped to clear the way for these ill-fated warships as they moved out of the frozen seas for that last naval clash of the Russo-Japanese War. Tragically, Admiral Makarov lost his life in the same conflict.

Between the two World Wars the icebreaker was used in the Murmansk area and the White Sea and also did sterling service on the Kara Sea route. She survived the Second World War to again do useful work for Russia. The *Yermack* was reported to have been broken up in the mid 1960s.

During the First World War a near sister to the *Yermack* was launched at Low Walker for the Russian government. Named the *Sviatogor*, she was needed for service in the Arctic seas off Murmansk and Archangel as the Baltic and Black Seas had been effectively closed to the passage of Russian and Allied

soon proving her worth by rescuing numerous ships stuck in the ice. The *Chronicle* reported: "During ten days cruising off Reval (Tallinn) it has rescued 31 ships from the ice, in which some of them had been embedded for several weeks."

The *Yermack* featured three engines aft driving triple propellers and a fourth engine in the bow to drive an icebreaking screw. The combined horsepower of these four main engines was 10,000. A large crew and about eighty passengers and cargo could be carried. The midships section of the hull was ships by the conflict.

Slightly larger than the *Yermack*, the *Sviatogor* was 323ft long and when she entered service was the largest icebreaker in the world. Three engines of a combined 10,000 horsepower were fitted, driving triple propellers.

Launched in 1916, she was delivered to her base at Archangel the following year but the outbreak of the Russian Revolution altered the course of her career. The Bolsheviks scuttled the ship in 1918 as they tried to block the port to British forces intervening in northern Russia against the revolution. However, the British raised the *Sviatogor*, repaired her and incorporated her into the Royal Navy for a few years. When the United Kingdom granted recognition to the Soviet government she was returned to Russia in late 1921.

In 1927 she was renamed the *Krasin* in a salute to L.B. Krasin, who was People's Commissar for Foreign Trade and the ship was again sent to the Arctic, being based at Murmansk. The following year she rescued members of an Italian airship expedition to the Arctic. Aircraft located the Italians' camp and the *Krasin* steamed towards their position and took them on board. In 1934 came another rescue. This time the crew of a steamer trapped in the ice were saved.

The Second World War saw the *Krasin* helping to convoy Allied ships carrying vital supplies for the war effort. In 1957-58 she underwent major rebuilding work and emerged with new engines and a new, modern superstructure and only one funnel instead of two. But the hull which had taken shape at the Low Walker Yard so many years before survived, a testament to the skills of her builders.

She was later used as a scientific research ship and renamed the *Leonid Krasin*. For a while she also became a floating power

*The odd-looking icebreaking train ferry **Scotia** (later renamed **Scotia I**), launched in 1901 for service across the Strait of Canso, Nova Scotia, Canada. On her trials, an onlooker watching the vessel from the Northumberland coast joked: "Whey, Geordie, there's Bedlington Colliery gannin awa' to sea." In 1915 the yard completed another train ferry for the same service, the **Scotia II.***

station in the Arctic. Eventually, the name *Leonid* was dropped and she reverted to being simply the *Krasin*. Still surviving, in 1989 the *Krasin* became a museum/research ship and the following year paid a visit to London's Tilbury Docks. Sadly, a planned trip to the Tyne did not materialise.

The final icebreaker from Low Walker was the *Alexander Nevski*, built in 1916-17 but not completed until after the Russian Revolution. Seized by the Royal Navy, she was renamed HMS *Alexander*. However, she was handed over to the Soviet government in the early 1920s and renamed *Lenin*. As we have seen, she often carried out duties on the Kara Sea route. The *Lenin* was reported to be still in service in the mid-1960s.

Low Walker's fleet of "oyster-openers" had enjoyed long and useful lives.

Launch Parties at Low Walker

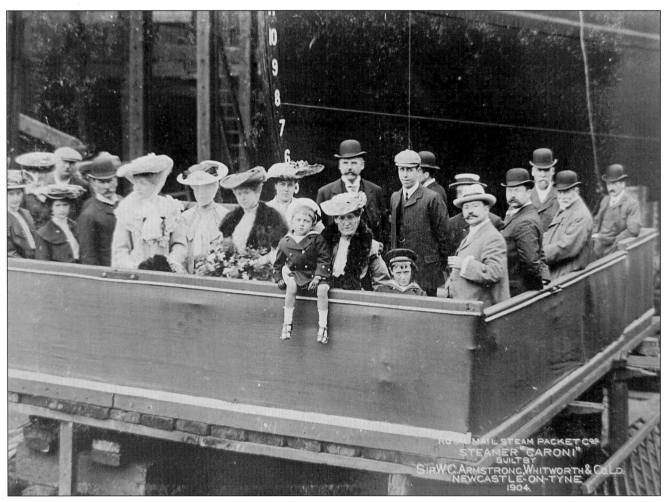

*Members of the launch party for the British cargo ship **Caroni** in 1904. Launches were social occasions with ladies in attractive hats very much in evidence. The **Caroni** was sunk by a U-boat in 1915.*

*The launch party for the British oil tanker **Beme** in 1904. A small girl has a day out to remember as she looks towards the camera with grown-ups at the head of the steps leading to the platform. The **Beme** had a long career, but was eventually sunk by the Italian submarine **Refado Tarantini** in the Mediterranean in 1940.*

Ladies in long dresses and splendid hats with a small boy are among the party on the launch platform for the Austro-Hungarian cargo ship **Atlantica** in 1911. She survived the First World War and changed ownership twice. Eventually the **Atlantica** was requisitioned by Britain during the Second World War but was bombed and sunk by German aircraft off Yarmouth, Isle of Wight, in 1941.

Oil Tankers

In 1881 the Low Walker Yard completed its first oil tanker, the *Massis*, for service in the Caspian Sea petroleum trade. She was equipped with one tank amidships designed to carry crude petroleum but also possessed an ordinary cargo hold. The following year saw the yard turning out two more tankers for the same trade, the *Poseidon* and *Armeniak.* Of these small ships, the *Armeniak* was the most significant for future developments since she was purely an oil tanker and carried no other cargo.

Within the following twenty years Low Walker was to establish itself as one of the world's leading builders of this type of vessel. Indeed, under the guidance of Charles Mitchell's able partner, Henry F. Swan, it was a pioneer of oil tanker design.

Henry took out several patents for tank steamers and became one of the world's foremost authorities in this field. His design ideas were embodied in the *Gluckauf*, which in 1886 became the first tanker to carry oil across the Atlantic. The vessel, which was built for shipowners Riedemann of Bremen, is generally regarded as the prototype of the modern oil tanker. The *Gluckauf*'s shell plating constituted an integral part of the oil tanks, which were divided into pairs by a middle line bulkhead. In each tank, the oil extended to the shell and deck. Machinery was placed aft, with a short bridge amidships.

The *Gluckauf* (German: Good luck) was launched into the Tyne on 16 June 1886, and underwent trials the following month. Shortly afterwards she departed on her maiden voyage to New York. The makers of barrels and tin cases for oil in the United States were alarmed by the arrival of this ship whose relatively large tanks were clearly a threat to their business. They managed, for a time at least, to persuade coaling agencies to withhold supplies of bunker coal from the *Gluckauf*. However, the ship overcame this difficulty and she loaded her liquid cargo. Re-crossing the Atlantic, she reached Geestemunde towards the end of August.

Unfortunately, the career of this pioneering ship lasted less than ten years. In 1893 she ran aground on Fire Island in the approaches to New York, being declared a total loss. The wreck was sold as scrap for a mere 350 dollars.

The yard went on to build more than 140 tankers. Most of these led mundane but highly useful lives transporting oil throughout the globe. However, the carriage of such an inflammable cargo has always been a potentially dangerous undertaking, and was particularly hazardous in the early years of the trade when the perils were not always fully appreciated. Low Walker's tankers were by no means immune from such accidents.

Among the ships which featured in the casualty figures was the *Ville de Calais*. Launched in August 1887 for French owners, she was fitted with triple expansion engines by the Wallsend Slipway and Engineering Company. Charles Mitchell and Henry F. Swan had been among the founders of this famous engineering concern.

In October 1888 the *Ville de Calais* arrived in the Dock Basin at Calais with a cargo of crude petroleum from America. Disaster struck on the 16th of the month when the tanker blew up. The explosion killed four men, injured a considerable number of other people and shattered windows in many parts of

*The Low Walker-built oil tanker **Lux**, launched in 1888. Three years later she was wrecked in the Mediterranean after catching fire.*

ballast tanks, which at the time were being pumped full of water. The flame may have ignited gas generated by the petroleum. Only ten people were aboard the *Ville de Calais* at the time of the blast. It is probable that loss of life would have been greater had more members of the twenty-six-man crew been present.

During the following year an attempt by a tug to tow the stern section of the wrecked tanker to London for scrap proved a disastrous failure. Off Margate the tow rope parted and the wreck sank. John Stanford, the man who had bought the remains of the ship, fell overboard from the tug and died of exposure.

The career of another Low Walker-built tanker, the *Lux*, also ended in tragedy. Completed in 1888 'on spec', she was sold to J.M. Lennard and Sons, of Middlesbrough. In 1889 the *Newcastle Daily Journal* told readers that the *Lux* had "just arrived in the Tyne from Philadelphia with a bulk cargo of petroleum equal to about 15,000 barrels, or a volume of 700,000 gallons. This is the largest tank steamer to bring its cargo to the Tyne across the Western Ocean".

Tragedy struck in the autumn of 1891 while the ship was bound for Antwerp from Batoum with a cargo of petroleum. While entering the Doro Channel near the Greek island of Negropol the vessel was hit by a fire which was soon out of control. Twenty people lost their lives, including Captain Brough, from Cumberland, his wife, two children and sister-

the town, apparently causing panic amongst residents.

The captain, his wife and another woman were aboard the vessel at the time but miraculously survived. When they emerged from their cabin in the after part of the vessel, which was the only section to remain intact, they were horrified to see that the rest of the ship, apart from a section of the forecastle, had been blown to pieces. The explosion threw fragments of the hull and machinery a long way from the dock. One piece of iron plating fell through the roof of a house. A soldier walking about a mile from the ship received a serious leg injury from one of the fragments.

There was speculation that the blast had been caused by an engineer taking a naked light into the hold to check the ship's in-law. There were only six survivors.

The blaze was believed to have originated in the coal bunkers and it seems likely that some of the oil she was carrying had leaked into this area and then into the stokehold bilge beneath the boilers. As the fire raged, the steamer grounded on the rocky shore of Negropol and an explosion occurred.

Accidents at sea did not always, of course, involve fire, explosion and loss of life. The Low Walker tanker *Beacon Light* struck an iceberg on her maiden voyage in May 1890 but managed to remain afloat and reach New York.

The vessel was launched into the Tyne on 2 March 1890. The *Newcastle Daily Chronicle* reported: "Yesterday there was launched from the Low Walker Yard a large screw steamer built on the Swan's patent for the carriage of petroleum in bulk. The ship was named the *Beacon Light* by Mrs Stewart of Liverpool. The vessel has been built for Messrs. R. Stewart & Co., who are amongst the largest importers of petroleum in Liverpool."

On 1 May the newspaper was reporting on the ship's trials: "After adjusting compasses the vessel made several runs on the measured mile and attained a mean speed of 11 knots. During the trial the machinery ran without the slightest hitch. The vessel returned to the Tyne for bunker coal before proceeding to sea on her first voyage."

The ship duly left for New York. On 13 May the *Beacon Light* encountered a mist which prevented the lookout men from seeing any great distance ahead. It was becoming colder but the captain did not suspect icebergs. Suddenly the lookout on the forecastle shouted: "Ice ahead!" A white mass towered over the tanker and shortly afterwards she struck a huge ice-

*The British oil tanker **Silverlip**. She was launched at Low Walker in November 1902. As well as carrying oil, she also burned oil as fuel for her engines and was a portent of the gradual decline in the use of coal at sea.*

berg. The officer of the watch had ordered the engines stopped and then reversed, but the ship's headway was too great to prevent the impact.

As the *Beacon Light* hit the berg a heavy pinnacle of ice, reportedly weighing fifty tons, fell off it onto the ship's bow, smashing in the steel deck. Some of the vessel's plates abaft the bow were also broken by the ice.

The ship was now holed in several places. Fortunately, these openings were largely plugged by ice and this may have helped to keep her afloat. Despite this, the sea poured into the forward compartment. The steam pumps were put into action and with difficulty the *Beacon Light* managed to limp into New York, albeit in a sinking condition. By this time she had more than 2,500 tons of water aboard. She was immediately put into dry dock. There does not appear to have been any injury or loss of life.

After this dramatic maiden voyage, the tanker lasted for

Umbrella time. It was a dull and rainy day when this picture was taken of the crowds at the launch of the tanker **Silverlip** *on 29 November 1902.*

guests of the Mayor and Corporation of Newcastle at the city's Grand Assembly Rooms.

Reporting the launch of the *Silverlip* the *North Mail* informed readers: "Not only will the vessel carry petroleum, but petroleum will be used for propelling her. It was a dull rainy day. The coaly Tyne was in its darkest mood and seemed to frown at the steamer that was the embodiment of the discovery of a fuel that would supplement the coal which made it so great a waterway.

"Special trains conveyed hundreds of prominent Newcastle folk to Walker. It was a distinguished company hidden beneath umbrellas that surrounded the towering bows of the new ship. Dangling over the bows was the usual bottle of wine, gorgeously draped with red, white and blue, and jealously guarded by a workman, who was holding a beautiful bouquet for the Lady Mayoress.

"Her ladyship turned the handle and there was a little click, which was the first remark of the new born vessel. The bottle was so graciously dashed against the side that a keen sighted workman, seeing the prospect of saving some of the precious liquid, commenced pulling it rapidly upwards. Another man hung over the bow and caught several drops in a grimy cap, whereat the crowd cheered."

Sadly the *Silverlip* went on to have a relatively short career. On 1 May 1907 she was abandoned on fire in the Bay of Biscay after an explosion in one of her cargo tanks. She had been carrying benzine. Five men lost their lives.

nearly twenty-eight years. However, her luck ran out in February 1918 when she was torpedoed and sunk by a U-boat fifteen miles south-east of the Butt of Lewis. She had been steaming from Liverpool to Scapa Flow naval base with fuel oil. Thirty-two men, including the captain, were killed.

On 29 November 1902 the oil tanker *Silverlip* was launched at Low Walker. It was evidently a grand occasion, for the chief guest was the Lord Mayor of London, Sir Marcus Samuel, chairman of the Shell Transport and Trading Co.

The previous day the Lord Mayor, the Lady Mayoress and the Sheriffs of London and their ladies had taken a journey down the river in the steamer *J.C. Stephenson* at the invitation of the River Tyne Commissioners. In the evening they were

Warships

*Sailors man the yards of the Chilean cruiser **Esmeralda**, as she lies at anchor in the Tyne following her completion in 1884 at Low Walker. The ship is saluting the Prince and Princess of Wales on the occasion of their visit to the Tyne to open the Coble Dene Dock (later the Albert Edward Dock) at North Shields. The royal couple are in the paddle steamer to the right of the picture, the **Para-E-Amazonas**, which was built by Andrew Leslie & Co. of Hebburn for service on the River Amazon.*

Although the Low Walker Yard was mainly renowned for its merchant vessels, its order books also featured a considerable number of warships. Russia was the first foreign navy to do business with Mitchell's when two naval tenders, the *Ijora* and *Slavianka,* were launched in 1861.

Soon, the Tsarist government was turning to Mitchell's to help the Russian Navy begin the transformation from wooden to iron warships. From 1863, under a special agreement, the company operated a yard in St Petersburg where five warships were built for the Russian Navy. Henry F. Swan went out to St Petersburg to direct operations, taking over from Charles Mitchell who had gone there to start off the venture. The company was thus helping to train the Russians in iron shipbuilding skills.

The first ships to be completed at the Russian yard under the supervision of Mitchell's were the coastal defence vessels *Smertch*

*The Japanese cruiser **Naniwa** (sometimes given her full name of **Naniwa Kan**). Launched at the yard in 1885, she fought the Chinese at the Battle of the Yalu in 1894 and the Russians at Tsushima in 1905. The victorious commander at Tsushima, Admiral Togo, had been captain of the **Naniwa** in his earlier years.*

(Waterspout) and *Netron Menya* (Touch Me Not) in 1865. The last of the five, the *Prince Pojarski*, was completed in 1873. Her main armament consisted of eight 9-inch guns. Equipped with engines, she was also a full-rigged sailing ship with three masts.

Meanwhile, in 1868, Low Walker had made a breakthrough into major new markets when the gunboat *Staunch* was delivered to the Royal Navy.

The *Staunch*, intended for coastal defence, had been designed by George Rendel, a partner at Armstrong's of Elswick. Along with Andrew Noble, Rendel had played a key role in building up the company's armaments empire. The launch of this gunboat at Low Walker marked the start of a long association between the firms of Armstrong and Mitchell which eventually led to their merger. Before the amalgamation, however, Armstrong's built only the guns and left the shipbuilding to Mitchell's.

The *Staunch* was 79ft long with a 25ft beam. She carried a single 9-inch gun mounted forward, in line with her keel. Within a few years orders were pouring into Low Walker for gunboats. During the 1870s and early 1880s the yard completed 21 of these vessels, including 11 for China, three more for Britain, two for Holland, and four for Australia.

Soon, however, the yard was building much larger warships. On 6 June 1883 the cruiser *Esmeralda* was launched at Low Walker. Built for Chile, she had been designed by George Rendel and was the first of a famous group of fast, hard-hitting, protected warships which became universally known as "Elswick Cruisers". The *Esmeralda* had a speed in excess of 18 knots.

Earlier, in 1880, three other cruisers built to less satisfactory designs had been launched at Low Walker, two of which were ordered by China. These ships, the *Chao Yung* and *Yang Wei*, were lost at the Battle of the Yalu, fought between the Chinese and Japanese in 1894. Gunfire from the Japanese ships set the *Chao Yung* on fire and she turned over and sank. Salvoes also set the *Yang Wei* ablaze and she ran aground. Wood in their superstructures and ornamentation had burned fiercely.

Low Walker and Elswick ships featured on both sides in this battle, which meant that Tyne-built vessels were fighting each other. They included Low Walker's *Naniwa* (sometimes referred to as the *Naniwa Kan*) which had been launched for the Japanese.

The cruiser *Naniwa* slid down the ways on 18 March 1885. The *Newcastle Daily Journal* reported: "The chocks having been knocked out, the vessel began slowly to descend towards the river. Just as it began to move Lady Armstrong dashed a bottle of champagne against the side of the ship ... A numerous and capable staff of Japanese constructors and engineers have supervised the progress of the work, which has been facilitated by their able and intelligent assistance in the arrangement of all important features..."

Following the launch, a dinner was held at the County Hotel, Newcastle, at which Sir William Armstrong presided. In a speech he told guests, who included Prince Yamashino of Japan, that "the ship that had been launched was for the service of a country which was never likely to come into collision with our own peace-loving country".

The *Naniwa* was completed in early 1886 and was moved down river to Jarrow Slake as preparations began for her delivery voyage. A Japanese crew had arrived on Tyneside to man her. But just as things seemed to be going well, tragedy struck. Takezo Fukamachi, who bore the rank of paymaster, had a serious fall while aboard the vessel and died from his injuries.

Under the heading "Death of a Japanese Officer at Jarrow", the *Journal* told readers: "On Saturday morning, Takezo Fukamachi, described as a paymaster on board the Japanese imperial war vessel now lying in the river at Jarrow Slake, died from injuries received on the previous evening. He fell down the hold of the vessel and concussion of the brain ensued. Ronosuko Sudsuki, the ship's surgeon, dressed the deceased's wounds and otherwise attended him." The inquest, held

The obelisk memorial to Takezo Fukamachi, paymaster of the Japanese cruiser **Naniwa**, *in St John's Cemetery, Elswick, Newcastle. The officer died of injuries as the result of a fall aboard the* **Naniwa** *while she was lying at Jarrow Slake.*

(Photo: Dick Keys)

*The Norwegian coast defence battleship **Harald Haarfagre** surrounded by guests and spectators before her launch in 1897. A sister ship, the **Tordenskjold,** was launched in the same year.*

part in the great naval clash between Russia and Japan at Tsushima in 1905. The victorious Japanese fleet at this battle was commanded by Admiral Heihachiro Togo.

In earlier years Togo had been captain of the *Naniwa*. The cruiser had intercepted a British merchant ship, the *Kow Shing*, carrying 1,500 Chinese troops to Korea on the outbreak of war between China and Japan in 1894. Controversially, the *Naniwa* sank the troopship after the Chinese refused to allow the British captain to surrender the vessel to Togo and accompany the *Naniwa* into port.

Two other Japanese cruisers, the *Takachiho* (or *Takachiho Kan*), a sister of the *Naniwa*, and the *Takasago* were built at Low Walker. The *Takasago* was lost when she struck a mine near Port Arthur in 1904. The *Takachiho* was sunk by enemy action in October 1914 off Tsingtau, China, with the loss of over 240 men. Accounts vary as to whether she was torpedoed or hit a mine.

Low Walker also built warships for customers much closer to home than Japan. In 1897 two Norwegian coastal defence battleships slid down the ways, the *Harald Haarfagre* and the *Tordenskjold*. The *Tordenskjold* was launched on 18 March of that year by Madam Nansen, wife of famed Arctic explorer Fridtjof Nansen. The ship had a long and useful career, but was captured by the Germans during the Second World War and eventually sunk by British air attack.

In 1898 a cruiser was launched 'on spec' at the yard in the knowledge that she was likely to find a buyer at a time when

aboard the *Naniwa*, recorded a verdict of "Accidental death".

The paymaster is buried in Elswick Cemetery, his grave marked by an impressive obelisk. It bears an inscription in both English and Japanese, which reads: "In memory of Jushichii Takezo Fukamachi, Imperial Japanese Navy, who was born on 18th May 1856, 4th Year of Ansei, and departed this life on the 19th February 1886." The *Newcastle Daily Journal* described the Japanese officer as "one who, by his kind disposition and gentlemanly bearing, won the respect and goodwill of all those who had the honour of his acquaintance".

The cruiser *Naniwa* left the Tyne for her voyage to Japan in late March 1886. As well as the Battle of the Yalu, she also took

Runaway ship. The launch party for the cruiser **Fourth of July,** *which entered the Tyne appropriately on 4 July 1898. The ship moved down the ways so rapidly that the lady who was to have launched her was unable to break the traditional bottle of wine over the vessel's bows. The ship was sold to Chile and renamed the* **Chacabuco,** *surviving until the early 1950s.*

A stern view of the Chinese cruiser **Chao Yung** *on the stocks at Low Walker in 1880. She was sunk by Japanese warships at the Battle of the Yalu in 1894.*

many fleets throughout the world were increasing their strength. The ship was named the *Fourth of July*, in honour of American Independence Day and fittingly she entered the Tyne on 4 July.

However, things did not go entirely to plan. Miss Watts (probably the daughter of the ship's designer, Philip Watts) was to perform the ceremony but after several attempts failed to break the bottle of wine against the vessel's bows, the ship moved swiftly away into the river. The bottle was left intact, although the spectators and workmen still cheered as the cruiser slid into the Tyne. But it was unthinkable that the ship should not have its traditional baptism and Miss Watts and officials boarded a steam launch, catching up with the newly water-borne vessel. The naming ceremony was duly performed on the river.

Despite this slight hitch, which may have worried superstitious seamen, the *Fourth of July* was successful in finding a buyer and had a long career. She was sold to the Chilean Navy and renamed *Chacabuco*. The vessel was not broken up until the early 1950s.

Among the other Low Walker vessels which had a long life was the self-propelled hopper barge *Drudge*, launched on 8 June 1887, which the *Newcastle Daily Journal* reported was "built to remove the firm's waste from Elswick" and went on to note that she was "so arranged that guns of 110 tons, or even heavier, can be mounted and taken out to sea for testing or, if required, used in warfare".

The humble *Drudge* made a surge up the social scale in February 1901 when she became a Royal Navy trials gunboat following acquisition by the Admiralty. Her naval career was to last for nineteen years. For a couple of these she bore the unlikely name *Excellent*. The *Drudge* eventually ended up in a French shipbreaker's yard after a remarkable life spanning eighty-two years. She was still using her original engines, built by the Wallsend Slipway and Engineering Company, until the very end.

The Final Years

On 31 December 1927 the firm of Armstrong Whitworth amalgamated some of its most important businesses with concerns owned by Vickers Ltd., of Barrow-in-Furness, to form Vickers-Armstrong Ltd. The Low Walker Yard, the Walker Naval Yard and the Elswick Works in Newcastle all came under the ownership of the new company.

However, Low Walker was leased back by Vickers-Armstrong to Sir W.G. Armstrong Whitworth & Co. Ltd. which still survived as a separate company. In 1929 this firm restructured its business so that a subsidiary company, Sir. W.G. Armstrong Whitworth & Co. (Shipbuilders) Ltd., took control of Low Walker and of the old Dobson Yard at Walker and the former Tyne Iron Shipbuilding Yard at Willington Quay.

It was not long, however, before these yards were experiencing the effects of the great Depression of the early 1930s. On 19 December 1930 the tanker *Elise* was launched into the Tyne from a Low Walker slipway for Norwegian owners. But the company's managing director, James Stewart, told guests: "We have launched today one of the highly specialised inventions

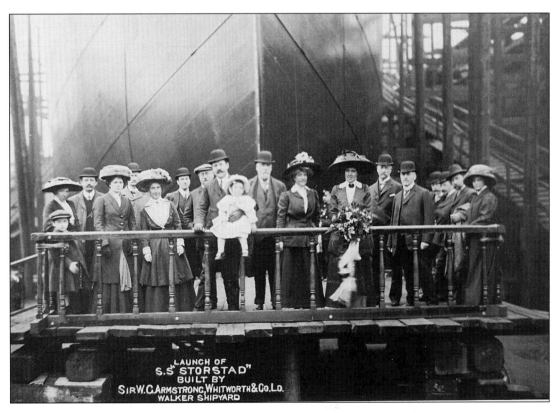

*A very smartly dressed group pose on the launch platform for the Norwegian cargo ship **Storstad** in 1911. Tragically, the **Storstad** hit the passenger liner **Empress of Ireland** in fog while in the St Lawrence River on 29 May 1914. The liner sank rapidly with the loss of 1,024 lives. It was one of the worst disasters in 20th century shipping history. The **Storstad** was sunk by a U-boat off Ireland in 1917.*

of man's ingenuity, an up to date tanker. Unfortunately, it leaves our shipbuilding berths at Walker absolutely empty, though we have one or two building in other yards."

The position did not improve to any great degree. In 1934 the Low Walker Yard closed. Sir W.G. Armstrong Whitworth & Co. (Shipbuilders) Ltd. sold the yard to National Shipbuilders Security Ltd. Low Walker had simply run out of orders and in the final year or two only a small number of men were employed.

National Shipbuilders Security Ltd. had been formed to purchase redundant or obsolete shipyards, dismantle them and dispose of their contents. It seemed the yard's life was at an end.

However, the outbreak of the Second World War brought renewed demand for ships. Low Walker's slipways reopened in 1942 under the Tyne Branch of the Shipbuilding Corporation Ltd. The yard was placed under the management of Armstrong Whitworth. A series of cargo vessels were constructed for the war effort and many older workers returned to contribute their skills and experience.

With the arrival of peace in 1945 Low Walker continued to operate. The work included the completion of several ships which had been ordered during the war and a series of self-propelled barges for the Irawaddy Flotilla Co.

The final ship from the Low Walker Yard was the cargo vessel *Zarian*, which had originally been ordered by the Ministry of War Transport with the intention of naming her *Empire Birdsay*. However, she was launched as the *Zarian* for the United Africa Co., on 16 August 1947. Later the ship was sold to the Palm Line and renamed *Lokoja Palm*. Speaking at the launch ceremony, Edwin Graham, general manager, praised the readiness with which older workers had returned to Low Walker to help meet the vital needs of wartime.

The yard closed in 1948 after a proud history during which management and workers had made a major contribution towards establishing the Tyne as one of the world's most important shipbuilding rivers. The shipyard founded by Charles Mitchell had lasted ninety-five years.

The final ship. The **Lokoja Palm***. She was launched on 16 August 1947 under the name* **Zarian***. The vessel was broken up in China in 1971.*

(Photo: John Clarkson, Longton)

Other Notable Ships
from the Low Walker Yard

Hooper, cable ship

When launched on 31 March 1873 the 4,935 gross ton *Hooper* was exceeded in size as a cable ship only by Isambard Kingdom Brunell's mammoth *Great Eastern*. The *Hooper* was the first vessel to be built specially for the trans-Atlantic telegraph cable service and arguably the first purpose-built cable layer ever constructed. A very large and complex vessel for her day, her owners required completion in only six months. Mitchell not only took up this demanding and very risky commercial challenge but went on to finish her in just ninety working days "deducting Sundays, holidays and wet" – a remarkable achievement. The *Hooper* (she was renamed *Silvertown* in 1881) was a very successful vessel and for over forty years laid cables in many parts of the world, including ones from Britain to Bermuda, Sydney to Auckland, New York to Cuba, San Francisco to Honolulu and Dakar to Pernambuco.

Train Ferry No. I and *Train Ferry No. II*

The simply named *Train Ferry No. I* and *Train Ferry No. II* (abbreviated to *T.F.1* and *T.F.2* when painted on their bows) were one of the most important contributions made by the yard to the war effort of 1914-18. They were built to carry train loads of weapons and stores across the Channel to the British Army on the Western Front. With its experience of constructing such specialist craft it is understandable why Armstrong Whitworth was selected for the contract for these ships and for much of the docking facilities for them built at Richborough on the Kent coast. At the time of their launch in 1917 *T.F.1* and *T.F.2* ranked amongst the largest ferries in the world. It was estimated that one of these ships could do the work of three

conventional cargo vessels. After the First World War the ferries were acquired by Great Eastern Train Ferries Ltd. and from 1924 ran very successfully on the company's Harwich to Zeebrugge service until the outbreak of the Second World War. The *T.F.2* became an early casualty. On 14 June 1940, when off St Valery en Caux, she was abandoned after being shelled by shore batteries. Fourteen of her crew were lost. *T.F.1* was re-named *Iris* (later changed to *Princess Iris*) following purchase by the Admiralty in 1940 for use as a landing ship. After the war she was returned to commercial use as the *Essex Ferry* and was broken up in 1957.

Baralong cargo steamer

The *Baralong* was launched on 12 September 1901 and had a remarkable career. It began with a commercial disaster. She was engaged to tow a newly-built floating dock from the Tyne to Durban, South Africa, a distance of about 7,090 miles. It was a job which would have been a handful for a couple of deep sea tugs, let alone an ordinary cargo steamer. But, had it not been for a storm encountered when about 500 miles from her destination, she would have made it. However, the towing hawsers parted and the dock drifted ashore near Mossel Bay to become a total wreck. During August 1905 the *Baralong* was in collision with the troop-laden steamer *Kinjio Maru* in the Sea of Japan. The steamer sank with the loss of 160 lives. Although damaged herself, the *Baralong*'s boats were lowered to help with the rescue work.

It was the *Baralong*'s run-of-the-mill appearance which led to her being commissioned into the Royal Navy as a 'Q' ship during the First World War. 'Q' ships were merchant vessels fitted with concealed guns. It was their role to lure German submarines to within range and open fire on them. For this purpose the *Baralong* was armed with three 12-pounder guns. On a calm day in August 1915, when patrolling off the south coast of Ireland, she came across the steamer *Nicosian* which was being attacked by the surfaced U-27. Hoisting the colours of then neutral America, and flying flags to indicate that she was approaching to pick up survivors, the *Baralong* drew close. It took the *Baralong*'s guns little over a minute to seal the U-27's fate. As she went down, her crew jumped in the water and swam towards the *Nicosian*, the ship they had been attacking and which had been abandoned. Six managed to climb aboard.

Concerned that they might finish off the *Nicosian* by fire or scuttling, the commander of the *Baralong* put his ship alongside and sent over a Royal Marine boarding party. None of the U-boat men lived to tell what happened.

These events were witnessed by the crew of the *Nicosian* which included American mule-teers – she was carrying a cargo of mules and fodder. When they returned home, some gave statements to the German ambassador to the United States and the Press, saying that the survivors had been killed in cold blood and that the *Baralong* was still under American colours when she first opened fire. These allegations were vigorously denied by the Admiralty who gave a different version of events. The '*Baralong* incident' remains one of the unsolved enigmas of the First World War. The ship survived until about 1933 when she was bought by Japanese breakers.

Tafelberg, floating whale oil factory

Launched on 29 April 1930, the 520ft-long whale oil factory *Tafelberg* was the largest vessel to be built at the Low Walker Yard and the largest in the South African merchant fleet at that time. Her 5,000 horsepower triple expansion steam engine was constructed at Armstrong Whitworth's Scotswood Works. Her owners were the Kerguelen Sealing & Whaling Company of Cape Town. Most of her whaling activities were carried out in Antarctic waters. However, the hunting of whales in the area was brought to a halt in January 1941 because of the Second World War and in the same month the *Tafelberg* struck a mine in the Bristol Channel and ran ashore, breaking her back. Declared a loss, that would normally have been the end of her but with substantial oil carrying capacity, plentiful accommodation and spacious decks, whale oil factories were proving

*(Above) The launch party for the Japanese oil tanker **Buyo Maru** in 1908. During World War I the ship served Britain as a fleet auxiliary tanker.*

themselves useful ships in the war situation. Bought by the Ministry of War Transport, the wreck was re-floated, repaired and brought back into service bearing the name *Empire Heritage*. On what turned out to be her last voyage she left New York in a convoy bound towards Liverpool with 16,000 tons of fuel oil, 1,900 tons of deck cargo, 73 D.B.S. (Distressed British Seamen, probably survivors from torpedoed ships), a crew of 77 and 11 gunners. As the convoy approached the north coast of Ireland in September 1944 it was sighted by the U-482 which unleashed a spread of torpedoes. One hit the *Empire Heritage*. She sank with the loss of over a hundred lives.

Beldis, heavy-lift vessel

The *Beldis* was the first of seven heavy-lift vessels built by Armstrong Whitworth for the Norwegian shipowner Captain Christen Smith between 1924 and 1927 and was a pioneer ship of her type. She, along with the *Belnor* and *Belray*, were constructed at the Low Walker Yard and the remainder at the Walker Naval Yard. Captain Smith's association with Armstrong Whitworth had begun some years before when he contracted to carry 200 locomotives and tenders which had been built at the company's Scotswood Works across to Antwerp without them having to be dismantled. The experience thus gained gave him the idea of having a specially designed heavy vessel with derricks capable of handling large weights, enabling her to use small, undeveloped ports which lacked the facilities for heavy cargoes. Armstrong Whitworth's naval architects converted his ideas into reality and the *Beldis* was born. On her maiden voyage, this highly specialised vessel carried locomotives to Argentina. The *Beldis* was available to serve the Allied cause during the Second World War when she sailed under the name *Herma*. She survived to have a long and chequered career during which she sailed under four national flags and had eight changes of name before being broken up in 1971.

Viking, passenger ferry

The two-funnel passenger ferry *Viking* (1,957 gross tons) was built for service between the Isle of Man and Lancashire. Ordered by the Isle of Man Steam Packet Co., she was launched in 1905. Her Parsons turbine engines were constructed by Wallsend Slipway and Engineering. The *Viking* achieved 24 knots on trials. During the First World War the ship served as a seaplane carrier. In 1919 she returned to the Isle of Man run and lived on to become a troopship during the Second World War. Afterwards, the *Viking* again returned to the Isle of Man service making her last voyage in 1954. Her career had lasted a magnificent forty-nine years.

Southern Cross, missionary ship

Headed by the Bishops of Newcastle, Durham and Wellington, New Zealand, no fewer than 112 clergymen and other church officials turned up to witness the launch of the *Southern Cross* on 12 February 1903. Built for the Melanesian Mission and christened by the widow of the second Bishop of Melanesia, she was a graceful, three-masted vessel with a clipper bow. Her figurehead was a beautifully carved depiction of St Barnabas. The *Southern Cross* was the fifth vessel of that name to serve the diocese of Melanesia which covered an area of some 200,000 square miles in the south-western Pacific, with over 170 missionary stations distributed among twenty-six different islands. Besides carrying stores and passengers, she also acted as a venue for religious instruction and services. The *Southern Cross* had a triple expansion steam engine of 117 horsepower and a substantial spread of sails which drove her along at 8.5 knots on her trials in a stiff westerly breeze off the Northumberland coast. For nearly thirty years, before ending her life in a New Zealand shipbreaker's yard, the *Southern Cross* set out from the mission's headquarters on Norfolk Island to make a series of cruises within the diocese, steaming in the dangerous and reef-strewn waters of the Pacific without any of the aids to navigation taken for granted today.

A Short Bibliography

Published Works

Cochrane A., *The Early History of Elswick* (Newcastle, 1909)

Colledge, J.J., *Ships of the Royal Navy*, Vol. 1 (Newton Abbot, 1969)

Hocking, C., *Dictionary of Disasters at Sea During the Age of Steam* (London, 1969)

Jentschura, H., Jung, D., Mickel, P., *Warships of the Imperial Japanese Navy, 1869-1945* (London, 1977)

Lloyd's of London, *Lloyd's War Losses – The First World War* (London, 1990)

Lloyd's of London, *Lloyd's War Losses – The Second World War* (London, 1989)

Marshall, J., *A Biographical Dictionary of Railway Engineers* (Newton Abbot, 1978)

McGuire, D.F., *Charles Mitchell* (Newcastle upon Tyne, 1988)

Meister J., *Soviet Warships of the Second World War* (London, 1977)

Mitchell, W.H., & Sawyer, L.A., *The Empire Ships*, second edition (London, 1990)

Newman, B. ed., *Catalogue of the Armstrong Collection of Tyne & Wear Museums* (Newcastle, 1994)

Ritchie C., *Q-ships* (Lavenham, 1985)

Rohwer J., *Axis Submarine Successes 1939-1945* (Cambridge, 1983)

Schell, W.A. compiler, *Register of Merchant Vessels Completed 1890-1904* (Lyndoch, Australia, 1988-1990)

The Shipyards of Armstrong Whitworth (undated)

Tennent, A.J., *British Merchant Ships Sunk by U-Boats in the 1914-1918 War* (Newport, Gwent, 1990)

Warren K., *Armstrongs of Elswick* (London, 1989)

Watts, A.J., *The Imperial Russian Navy* (London, 1990)

Newspapers

Newcastle Courant
Newcastle Daily Chronicle
Newcastle Daily Journal
Newcastle Daily Leader
The Times

Unpublished MS

Dobson, J. *List of New Vessels Using Northumberland Dock – 1858 to 1879*

Newcastle Libraries, *Armstrong Mitchell Cuttings Books*

Periodicals

Armstrong Whitworth Record
The Engineer
Engineering
Illustrated London News
Journal of the Society of Arts
Marine News
Nautical Magazine
Paddle Wheels
Sea Breezes
The Shipbuilder
Shipbuilding & Shipping Record
Polar Record
United States Naval Institute Proceedings
Warship International

Registers and Annual Publications

Janes Fighting Ships
Lloyd's Register of Shipping
Mercantile Navy List & Maritime Directory